The Oracle's Secret

**An Inspiring Fable About
Achieving Your Dreams**

Dr. Anthony Fernando

ℙℙ

Paxton Press

This book is dedicated
to my parents

Copyright © 2005 Anthony Fernando

National Library of Australia

Cataloguing in Publication data

Fernando, Anthony, 1970- .

The Oracle's Secret : an inspiring fable about achieving your dreams.

ISBN 0 646 45269 X.

I. Title.

A823.4

First edition published in 2005 by
Paxton Press Victoria

www.PaxtonPress.com

Acknowledgements

I would like to thank the following people who provided valuable feedback during the development of this book: Anderson, Marlon and Michael Fernando, Stephanie and David Bromage, Julie Davey, Vanessa McCallum, Rebecca Crea, Eugene Ware, Tessa Mellow, Tim O'Hagan, Philip Johnston and Margaret Holden. Your comments, support and assistance were very much appreciated.

A Boy and His Dream

Taran emerged from the village bakery and stepped into the warm morning sun. It was market day, and the village square was filled with bustling crowds and traders shouting their wares.

On the opposite side of the square, Taran saw a group of children gathered around the public notice board. Even from a distance he could tell something was going on.

As he made his way through the crowd, Taran's best friend, Olek, turned from the board and gestured to him to hurry.

"Taran, the Elders have announced a race to celebrate the Summer Solstice," said Olek excitedly, "and the prize is a stallion from the Alder Stables!"

Taran edged his way to the front of the group to view the notice board for himself. When he read the parchment his eyes widened and his heart skipped a beat.

It was true!

The Elders had organized a race to the top of Falcon

Ridge that would take place on the eve of the Summer Solstice. The race was open to all village children, and the winner would receive a stallion of their very own from the Alder Stables.

Taran couldn't believe his eyes. For as long as he could remember, he had dreamed of having his own stallion. Often on his way home from school, he would stop by the Alder Stables and watch the apprentices work with the horses.

The Alder Stables were the most famous horse training institution in the land of Etania.

Wealthy merchants traveled many leagues to purchase stallions from the stables, and now here was a chance for Taran to win a stallion of his very own!

After reading the notice board three more times just to make sure it was real, Taran and Olek moved aside to allow other children to view the announcement. By now, word of the race had spread, and it seemed as though every child in the village was gathered in the square.

"Are you going to enter?" asked Olek.

"Of course I am, and so are you," replied Taran.

"Nah, I'll never win…"

"Oh Olek, how do you know if you don't even try?"

"I'm just not a good runner."

"Well, I'm not the best runner in the village either, but to win a stallion from the Alder Stables I'd run to the edge of the world and back!"

"I bet Lomak is going to enter," said Olek a little dejectedly. Lomak was the biggest and strongest boy in the village. Although he was only a year older than Taran and Olek, he seemed as strong as some of the village men.

"Hmmm, you're right," replied Taran frowning. The two friends paused to watch a juggler entertaining the crowd with his skill and comical antics.

"My mother told me to be home by midday," said Olek, glancing up at the sun. "I'd better get going."

"Alright Olek, I'll see you at school," replied Taran. With a quick wave, Olek disappeared into the passing parade of horse-drawn wagons and carts.

As Taran browsed through the market stalls, he continued to think about the race and about Lomak.

In just about every sporting competition ever held in the village, Lomak had featured in the winning circle. Now, with a stallion from the Alder Stables on offer, Taran was sure that Lomak would enter the Summer Solstice Race.

He decided to discuss the upcoming event with his Uncle Seth.

Uncle Seth was the village blacksmith, and Taran loved spending time with him while he pumped the hefty bellows and filled the air with glowing sparks.

Taran made his way to Ironcraft Lane and entered the forge, where he heard his uncle pounding metal on metal. There was a pause, and then a loud hiss as

Uncle Seth plunged the red-hot metal into a tub of water, which instantly vaporized to fill the forge with steam.

Uncle Seth looked up from his work and wiped a soot-covered hand across his brow.

"Hey there Taran, how're ye doing?" came his uncle's familiar accent.

"I'm great Uncle Seth; how are you?"

"Well, there's food on the table and plenty of work that needs a doin', so I can't complain. What can I do for ye lad?"

"Have you got a few minutes?"

"Always got time for my favorite nephew. Let me just put this lot away and I'll be right with ye."

While his uncle put away his tools, Taran looked around the forge in admiration. Although Seth Eldridge was a humble man, it was well known around the village that he was a master of his craft. He regularly received commissions from neighboring villages, which was a true testament to his skill.

Taran and his uncle stepped out of the forge into a small courtyard, where they sat down at a wrought-iron table. Uncle Seth pulled two apples from the deep pockets of his apron and tossed one to Taran.

As Taran sank his teeth into the delicious fruit, he told his uncle about the Summer Solstice Race, the incredible prize on offer, and about Lomak.

"You're right Taran, young Lomak is a strong lad and he'll be hard to beat, but there's an old saying that 'the race doesn't always go to the fleetest of foot.'"

"What do you mean?" asked Taran curious.

"Well, I'm not really an expert in these things, but it sounds to me like ye have set your heart on winning this race."

"I'd do anything to have my own stallion," said Taran intently.

"Well, in that case, here's my advice to ye… When a young man comes of age and sets his mind on achieving a particular end, it's time for him to consult with the Oracle."

As a boy, Taran had heard stories about the Oracle but had dismissed them as bedtime fairy tales.

"You mean the Oracle really exists?"

"Aye, he exists alright, and he, better than anyone, can tell ye how to make your dreams a reality."

"So how do I find this Oracle?"

"He lives in a cave about halfway up Ridley Peak. You can get to the cave by following the deer trail that emerges from the forest."

"But what do I tell him?"

"Just tell him what's in your heart lad, and he'll take it from there. The Oracle has a way of always knowing the right thing to say."

"Did you see the Oracle when you were my age, Uncle?"

"Aye, that I did, and so too did your dad. We had our turn and now it's your turn. Mind ye don't discuss this with your friends though. They'll find out about the Oracle when their time comes."

"So I just follow the deer trail up Ridley Peak, find the Oracle, and ask him how to win the Summer Solstice Race?"

Uncle Seth smiled knowingly, "It may not turn out quite like that, but it sounds like a good place to start. So will ye do it?"

"You bet I will Uncle Seth! I'll go right after I finish my chores tomorrow."

"Well done boyo, and may the Gods go with ye."

The Oracle

Early the next morning Taran awoke to do his daily chores, which consisted of feeding the animals and collecting the eggs from the hen house.

To his surprise, when he got to the kitchen, his mother was already busy preparing breakfast, and a carry bag sat open on the table.

"You'll be needing something to eat on your trip," she said, bustling around the pantry.

"How did you know?"

"Uncle Seth stopped by last night," his mother replied.

"Well, I'll just do my chores and… "

"There'll be no chores today, Taran. It's time to go."

Taran was a little taken aback by his mother's words. He tried to match her somber countenance and sat down to eat his breakfast in silence. As he ate, he glanced up and caught his mother looking at him with a sad smile on her face.

When he was done, Taran picked up the carry bag and slung it across his shoulders.

"Just speak from your heart son and everything will be fine," said his mother fussing over him as he made his way to the door.

"I will," replied Taran a little puzzled. His uncle had told him to speak from his heart as well, but he wasn't really sure what that meant.

As Taran approached the door, his mother hugged him tight and said, "May the Gods bless you, Taran."

"Don't worry Mother, I'll be fine," said Taran, a little embarrassed. He had thought he was just going to climb Ridley Peak, ask the Oracle about the race and be back in time for dinner, but from his mother's behavior, he knew that this trip was somehow more important than he'd realized.

As he stepped out into the chill morning air and started down the path that led to Ridley Peak, he knew without looking back that his mother was watching him from the window.

The spring morning was alive and fresh, and Taran made good time through the sparse undergrowth. Birds filled the air with morning song, and the cool breeze lifted Taran's spirits.

Before long, Taran found himself at the base of Ridley Peak, an ominous-looking mountain whose summit disappeared into the clouds above. He walked through the foothills until he found the deer trail his uncle had told him about.

The track wound up through the trees, and was overgrown in many places, making it difficult to follow at times. The breeze stirred the leaves, causing the sunlight to dance on the path in mesmerizing patterns.

Taran hummed a song he had heard his uncle singing in the forge. He didn't know the words but the tune matched the rhythm of his step as he made his way along the trail.

After some time, Taran looked up at the sun to gauge how long he'd been traveling, and decided to stop for a drink and an apple. While he sat by the path, he became aware of the distant sound of running water.

The sound gradually increased in volume as he resumed his journey. Soon it drowned out everything else, and Taran realized it must be the river Minrod, which originated in the upper reaches of the mountains and supplied the village with fresh water.

The path continued on and up, until Taran made his way around a final bend, and came face-to-face with the mighty river.

He had emerged from the cover of the trees into a clearing, and the river flowed fast and wide in front of him. To his dismay, Taran saw that the deer trail continued on the opposite bank, but there was no obvious way to cross the raging waterway.

Taran surveyed his surroundings, and saw a stone pillar nearby. On the side of the pillar was a sign that read:

"If it is the Oracle you seek,
Be prepared to get wet feet"

Taran smiled warily as he read the sign. Clearly, the author had a sense of humor, but Taran knew that crossing the river was not going to be easy.

He removed his sandals, hooked the straps together and slung them around his neck. Then he took a deep breath and stepped into the fast-flowing river. He gasped as the freezing water circled his feet and legs.

The icy current tore at Taran's clothes like a million tiny knives and the water level rose quickly until it reached his chest. Taran sucked in his breath and tried to keep moving but his feet were numb, and the raging river was too strong. Suddenly, he lost his footing and was plunged into the freezing torrent.

Taran's arms flailed wildly as the mighty river Minrod swept him along like a tiny rag doll. He broke the surface and sucked in some precious air before kicking out as hard as he could to try and reach the opposite bank.

He wasn't a strong swimmer, but his days of playing in the swimming hole served him well, and slowly he edged his way closer to the river bank.

Finally, after what seemed like an eternity, Taran painfully dragged himself up on to the opposite bank.

He was exhausted, and for a long time just lay still, gulping air into his aching lungs.

Little by little, Taran's heart slowed to its regular rhythm and he was able to breathe normally. He picked himself up, squeezed the water from his clothes, and made his way back along the river bank.

The current had carried him a long way downstream, and the sun was high in the sky by the time he found the deer trail again.

Thankfully, Taran saw that the way ahead was a little easier and he pushed on with new resolve.

The morning sun gradually dried Taran's damp clothes, and he noticed that the terrain around him was changing. The trees were thinning, and the path ahead became more and more rocky.

Soon he was scrambling over loose stones and realized he had left the foothills behind. Little by little, the rocky path gave way to a set of rough handholds in the side of the mountain and Taran carefully started to climb.

As he rose higher and higher, the temperature dropped, even though the sun still shone high overhead.

With aching arms and legs, Taran pulled himself up over a ridge and onto a plateau from where he could see the entire valley. He looked back and saw the trail behind him disappearing into the distance.

He had reached his destination. Set high amongst the rocks was the entrance to a cave.

Taran scrambled up the slope, and saw that a horn made of pearl and wood was hanging from a stone pillar, similar to the one he had seen by the river.

A sign below the horn read:

> If you are worthy then
> sound the great horn.
> The unworthy will wish
> they'd never been born.

Taran unhooked the horn from the pillar, took a deep breath, and blew with all his might. The ancient horn produced a strong, pure tone that echoed out across the valley.

As Taran put the horn back on the pillar, a blast of savage, icy wind erupted from the cave entrance and slapped him in the face. From the depths of the cave a thunderous voice boomed:

"Who dares summon the Oracle?"

Taran shielded his eyes from the fierce wind and said,

"My name is Taran Eldridge."

There was a pause as the bitter wind continued to swirl around the entrance of the cave.

"Be gone Taran Eldridge! The Oracle does not consult with children. Return to your village or else you will die a slow and painful death!"

Taran wasn't sure what to do. The wind whipped at his hair and blew dust into his eyes but he stood his ground. The Oracle's comment brought the blood rising to his cheeks. How dare he call Taran a child!

Something stirred deep within Taran's chest. He remembered what his uncle and mother had said about speaking from the heart. He stood up straight and in a powerful voice he announced:

"My name is Taran Eldridge, and I have come to speak with the Oracle."

The wind subsided instantly, and all was calm. From behind him, Taran heard a gentle voice say, "Welcome Taran Eldridge, I've been expecting you."

Taran whirled around and came face-to-face with the Oracle.

The first thing Taran noticed about the old man was his twinkling eyes, which seemed to shine out from his face like two bright beacons. Lines of mirth creased his face, and his gentle smile radiated a sense of warmth and peace.

"Come young one, walk with me," said the Oracle as he moved away from the cave entrance.

"But the voice from the cave…" said Taran confused.

"Ah yes, the cave. You'd be amazed at how many boys and girls simply give up and walk away when they are challenged, but I'm glad to see you stood your ground. I thought you would." The Oracle walked briskly with the aid of a large wooden staff, and Taran had to pick up his pace to keep up.

"I suppose you could call the river and the cave my little tests to ensure that the young men and women I help have the right attitude. So tell me young one, why have you come?"

Taran told the Oracle about the race to be held on the Summer Solstice and about his dream of owning a stallion from the Alder Stables. He also told the Oracle about Lomak, and the fact that he had won almost every sporting competition ever held in the village.

As Taran spoke, the Oracle led him to a vantage point on the side of the mountain from which they could see the whole valley spread out below. They sat on two smooth boulders and continued to talk.

"My uncle said you could help me make my dream a reality. So I've come to ask you how I can win the race."

"Well young one, only you can make your dreams a reality, but I can offer you the wisdom I have if you'll agree to forge a Pact."

In Taran's village a Pact was an agreement made between adults. Once a Pact was forged, it could not be broken. Indeed, an individual's honor depended on keeping true to the Pacts they had forged.

One of the worst crimes someone could commit in the eyes of the villagers was to dishonor a Pact. Taran had never forged a Pact before, but he was pleased to see the Oracle was now treating him as an adult.

There was a set ritual to establishing a Pact, and Taran knew it well from observing his uncle dealing with customers in the forge.

"What are the conditions of the Pact you propose?" asked Taran to begin the ritual.

"First, you must agree to meet with me whenever I summon you, until our Pact is complete," replied the Oracle.

"Agreed," said Taran formally.

"Next, you must take action on the advice I give you."

"Agreed."

"Finally, no matter what happens, you must not give up until our Pact is complete."

"Agreed," said Taran. He grasped the Oracle's right forearm with his right hand and crossed his left hand over to grasp the Oracle's left forearm. At the same time, the Oracle's hands gripped Taran's forearms firmly.

"And so our Pact is forged," they repeated together.

"So, when do we begin?" asked Taran expectantly.

"The best time to begin something important is always *NOW!*" said the Oracle with a smile, and he set off at a brisk pace.

Lessons of Wisdom

The Oracle led Taran to another cave entrance. In contrast to the forbidding opening he had stood before earlier, this cave seemed warm and welcoming. Taran took the seat that was offered to him and realized he had entered the Oracle's home.

The walls of the cave were lined with shelves housing thick leather-bound books. Flasks of multicolored potions bubbled away quietly on a crowded bench top, and in the corner stood a bed with a patchwork quilt over it.

The old man went to the back of the cave and rummaged about in the dark before reappearing with a large scroll in his hands.

With an air of formality, he handed the scroll to Taran saying, "The First Lesson of Wisdom."

Taran eagerly unclasped the seal on the scroll and rolled it open on the table. The ancient-looking parchment contained the following message:

The starting point
of all success is to
give thanks for
that which you
already have

"What does it mean?" asked Taran a little confused. He couldn't see how this message was going to help him win a race to the top of Falcon Ridge.

"Young one, as you grow older you'll find that many people spend their time complaining about what is missing from their lives, instead of being thankful for what they have.

"What they don't realize is that the more they complain, the worse things become. Eventually, they wake up expecting bad things to happen, and all too often their fears become their reality."

Taran knew that what the Oracle said was true. He had often wondered why adults always seemed so negative, angry and upset.

"But how can I use this lesson to help me win the race?" he asked.

"By being thankful for all the good things in your life, you open the door and make room for all achievement and success.

"Here is what I want you to do. Take this parchment and write down all the good things you have in your life today.

"Include things like your health, your body, your family and friends, your village and anything else you are truly grateful for.

"Yes Sir…" said Taran a little doubtfully. He had been hoping that the Oracle was going to reveal a secret that would help him run faster. Instead, he had told him to give thanks to the Gods. This was all well and good, but how was it going to help him beat Lomak?

Remembering the Pact he had forged, Taran decided to put his doubts aside for a moment and concentrate on the task at hand.

After thinking about his life carefully, he wrote the following list on the parchment the Oracle had given him:

- Thank you for my health and my body

- Thank you for my mother and Uncle Seth, and for the love and support they give me

- Thank you for my friends Olek and Tegan

- Thank you for our wonderful village

- Thank you for all the opportunities I have

"Excellent," said the Oracle after reading Taran's finished list. "Now, every morning as soon as you wake up, I want you to spend a few minutes giving thanks to the Gods for all of these things, and then finish by saying thank-you for the day ahead."

"Yes Sir," said Taran. He was still a little disappointed that the Oracle had not told him anything directly related to the race, but he had forged a Pact, and he knew he was bound by that Pact to do as the Oracle requested.

"Sir, you said that you would summon me when you want to see me again. How will you summon me from here?"

"A very good question, young one!" The Oracle moved to a nearby shelf and returned carrying an ornately carved wooden box. Taran undid the intricate clasp and lifted the lid to reveal a blue, oval-shaped stone about the size of his palm. It was smooth to the touch and felt heavy as he lifted it out of the box.

"This is truly a gift from the Gods," said the Oracle. "It is a calling stone. Keep it by your bed, and when I wish to see you again, the calling stone will turn red."

"But how does it work?" asked Taran, amazed.

"Some things are best left unexplained young one. This calling stone has been passed down in my family for many generations, and I am now lending it to you until our Pact is complete."

"Thank you, I'll look after it," said Taran still in awe.

Taran made his way out of the Oracle's cave, and after wrapping the calling stone carefully, he turned for home. He was not looking forward to crossing the river Minrod again, but when he came to the waterway he found that a new sign had been posted on the bank.

Well done young one,
Now journey home.
To avoid a swim,
Use the stepping stones.

At the end of the sign was an arrow that pointed to the left. Taran followed the path until it curved around a bend, and to his relief he discovered there was indeed a set of stepping stones that would make crossing the river a lot easier.

When he arrived home, Taran found his mother and Uncle Seth waiting expectantly by the door.

After he explained what had happened, Uncle Seth let out a bellow of delight and slapped him hard across the back. "Well done boyo, I knew you'd stand your ground!" he said with glee.

Taran's mother wasn't quite so boisterous but she gave him a hug and said, "Congratulations son," and Taran could see tears of pride welling up in her eyes.

After a wonderful meal and a few of Uncle Seth's stories in front of the fire, Taran decided it was time for bed.

As he got up from his chair his Uncle said, "Whatever the Oracle has told you to do is for your ears only lad. But make sure you follow his instructions, even if they seem a little strange at first."

"I will Uncle Seth, thanks," said Taran.

He went into his room and carefully unwrapped the Oracle's calling stone. The stone was still a deep shade of blue and Taran placed it gently on his bedside table before turning out his lamp and going to sleep.

The Plan

Over the next few days, Taran woke up and immediately did as the Oracle had instructed. He climbed out of bed, rubbed the sleep out of his eyes and slowly and deliberately recited the following:

- Thank you for my health and my body
- Thank you for my mother and Uncle Seth, and for the love and support they give me
- Thank you for my friends Olek and Tegan
- Thank you for our wonderful village
- Thank you for all the opportunities I have
- Thank you for the day ahead

The first few times he tried this he really didn't see the point and felt a bit foolish, but then a funny thing started to happen.

As he recited the things he was thankful for, he actually started to *feel* thankful for things he usually took for granted, like his health and family.

Taran also discovered that by starting his day this way, he somehow ended up being in a better mood for the rest of the day.

The more thankful he became, the more impact it seemed to have.

He also found that it made him treat people differently. For example, instead of taking his mother for granted, he started thanking her for all the little things she did to help him every day.

He also came to appreciate his friends more and really enjoyed the time he spent with them.

Indeed, after about two weeks of his new morning routine, Taran decided that perhaps the Oracle really did know what he was talking about.

One evening, as he was getting ready for bed, Taran noticed that the Oracle's calling stone had changed color from its normal blue to a deep shade of red.

He picked up the stone expecting it to be warm but it was still cool to the touch and Taran wondered yet again how it worked.

The next morning, Taran set off for his second meeting with the Oracle. It was a day of rest, which meant he did not have to go to school and he was eager to talk to the Oracle again.

He gratefully used the stepping-stones to avoid another drenching, and arrived at the cave as the sun peeked over the valley walls.

"Come in, young one," said a voice from inside.

Taran entered the cave to find the Oracle at his bench busily adding ingredients into a large pot, which was boiling over an open flame.

Taran's first thought was that the Oracle was preparing a potion that would help him win the race, but his hopes were dashed as the Oracle approached with two steaming mugs and said, "Herbal tea to soothe your mind and body."

"Thank you," said Taran, trying to hide his disappointment. The Oracle settled into his chair and asked, "So young one, did you follow your first lesson?"

"Yes Sir, I did," replied Taran sipping his tea.

"And what did you discover?"

"Well, at first, I must admit I thought I was wasting my time and only did it because we had forged a Pact, but then after a while I actually found that it made me feel good to be grateful for all the things in my life."

"And what else did you learn?"

"I learnt that it's a good way to start the day because it means I don't take the things and people in my life for granted. I think it helps me be nicer to my family and friends because I appreciate them more."

"You have learnt your lesson well, young one."

The Oracle rose from his chair and moved to the back of the cave. He returned to the table carrying another well-worn scroll.

"The Second Lesson of Wisdom," said the Oracle, handing Taran the scroll. He rolled it out on the table top and read:

To gain your
heart's desire,
you must create
a plan of action

Even though the Oracle's first lesson had been useful, Taran had been hoping that this time his lesson would be more directly related to winning the race.

He was again a little disappointed, but he tried not to show it.

"I'm not sure I understand what it means by heart's desire," he said respectfully.

"Your heart's desire is something you have a true and deep longing for. Something that stirs you from within. Something you would do anything to achieve."

Taran thought about the Oracle's explanation for a moment and then replied carefully, "In that case, I think I do already know what my heart's desire is."

"Tell me young one."

"My heart's desire is to own a pure white stallion from the Alder Stables."

"Good! The first step in getting what you want from life is to decide what it is you want."

"Well, that's pretty obvious isn't it?" asked Taran a bit puzzled.

"You would think so young one, but many people never decide what they really want from life. Instead, they just plod along from day to day, and hope that the Gods will grant them success."

"And do the Gods ever help them?" asked Taran.

"Young one, even the Gods cannot help those who do not know what they want."

"So how do I make my heart's desire come true?" asked Taran.

"Aaah, now we come to the main part of our lesson," replied the Oracle. He pulled out a fresh piece of parchment and placed it in front of Taran.

"For your dream to come true in the real world young one, it must first become a reality in your mind. So the first step is to write your goal at the top of your parchment as though it has already come true."

Taran thought about this for a moment, picked up a delicate feather quill and carefully wrote:

I own a pure white stallion from the Alder Stables

The Oracle nodded after reading Taran's goal and said, "Good, now the next step is to draw a picture of your goal below your statement."

Taran had always enjoyed drawing, and he had been drawing horses for as long as he could remember. He dipped his quill into the small inkwell and drew the following picture below his goal.

My Goal

I own a pure white stallion from
the Alder Stables

"Very good young one. Now, below your drawing I want you to describe in detail what it will be like when you achieve your goal.

"First, see it in your mind's eye. Then describe what you are doing, and how you are feeling after accomplishing your goal."

Taran closed his eyes and imagined that he really did own a stallion from the Alder Stables. He thought about what he would do and how it would feel. Then he opened his eyes and wrote:

"I am enjoying the thrill of riding my pure white stallion through the hills of Etania. I can feel the cool breeze on my face and hear the wind roaring in my ears. I feel happy and proud as people from the village wave at us as we gallop by at full speed!"

"Excellent," said the Oracle after reading Taran's description. "The next step is to rule a line on the side of your parchment and write down 'My Plan – To achieve my goal I will:'"

Taran did as the Oracle instructed, and his parchment looked like this:

My Goal

I own a pure white stallion from the Alder Stables

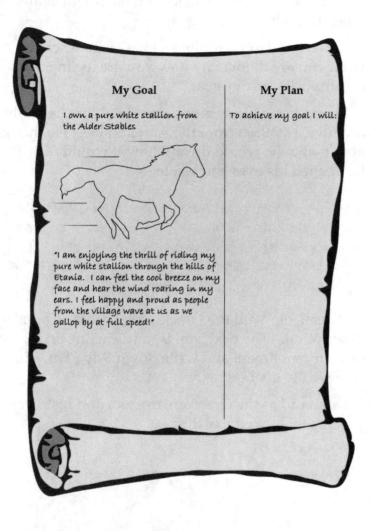

"I am enjoying the thrill of riding my pure white stallion through the hills of Etania. I can feel the cool breeze on my face and hear the wind roaring in my ears. I feel happy and proud as people from the village wave at us as we gallop by at full speed!"

My Plan

To achieve my goal I will:

"Now young one, remember what I said the first time we met. Only you can make your dreams a reality.

"I can guide you, but you will find that the knowledge you seek is already within you. All you have to do is ask the Question of Power."

"What is the Question of Power?" asked Taran hoping the Oracle was finally going to reveal something that would give him a magical advantage.

"The Question of Power is this –

'What do I need to do to achieve my goal?'"

Taran again felt a twinge of disappointment. Instead of a magical spell, the Question of Power seemed pretty straight-forward, but he now knew better than to question the Oracle.

He reread his goal and looked at the picture of the stallion he had drawn. As he did so, he said out loud, "What do I need to do to achieve my goal?"

As Taran cleared his mind and focused on the question at hand, ideas and thoughts started popping into his head. After a moment's reflection he said, "To achieve my goal I need to win the race."

"Good young one, now take the answer your mind has given you and ask the Question of Power again."

Taran was starting to see how the Question of Power worked. He took the answer to his first question and asked out loud, "What do I need to do to win the race?"

As soon as he had asked this question, he realized he again already knew the answer.

"To win the race I need to improve my running skills."

"Excellent, young one," encouraged the Oracle. "Ask the Question of Power again!"

Taran started to feel a stirring in the room. It really did feel like there was something magical going on each time he asked the Question of Power.

He heard himself say, "What do I need to do to improve my running skills?" Once again, as soon as he had asked the question, an answer popped into his mind. This time the answer was,

"I need to practice everyday."

"Ask again young one!" said the Oracle.

Taran took his answer and asked, "What do I need to do to practice everyday?" Yet again he found that when he asked the question, he already knew the answer –

"I need to wake up early and go running up Falcon Ridge before school."

"Very good, young one. The Question of Power is the key to the endless wisdom that lies within each of us. Now I want you to take your answers and use them to create a step-by-step plan and write it down on your parchment."

Taran turned to his parchment and realized the Question of Power had indeed revealed exactly what he needed to do to make his dream a reality.

Using the answers to the questions he had asked, Taran formulated the following plan:

1. Wake up early

2. Practice running up Falcon Ridge each morning before school

3. Gradually improve my running skills

4. Win the race

5. Collect my stallion from the Alder Stables

The Oracle reviewed Taran's plan and nodded, "Good, young one."

"Now, the final step is to set a date by which you will complete your plan. Many people forget to do this and a goal without a target date is nothing but a wish."

Taran considered the Oracle's statement and replied, "Well the race is on the eve of the Summer Solstice, so I suppose my target date is the following morning."

"Very good, now write it down."

Taran's finished parchment looked like this:

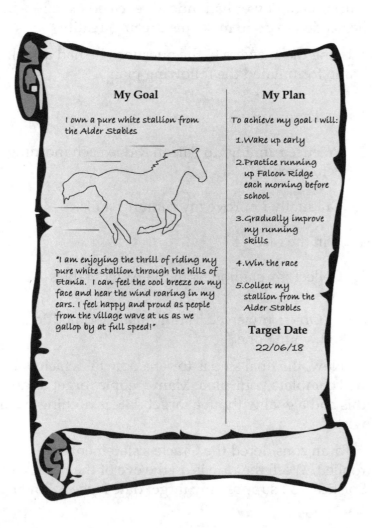

My Goal

I own a pure white stallion from the Alder Stables

"I am enjoying the thrill of riding my pure white stallion through the hills of Etania. I can feel the cool breeze on my face and hear the wind roaring in my ears. I feel happy and proud as people from the village wave at us as we gallop by at full speed!"

My Plan

To achieve my goal I will:

1. Wake up early

2. Practice running up Falcon Ridge each morning before school

3. Gradually improve my running skills

4. Win the race

5. Collect my stallion from the Alder Stables

Target Date

22/06/18

"You have done well today, young one. You have identified your heart's desire. You have set a goal and used the Question of Power to create a plan for making your dream a reality. Until we meet again, here is what I want you to do.

"Each morning when you wake up:

- Start your day by giving thanks to the Gods for the good things in your life and for the day ahead;

- Read your goal out loud;

- Look at the picture you have drawn;

- Read the description of your dream out loud;

- Close your eyes and imagine yourself living out your dream;

- Put your plan into action.

"Then, each evening before you go to sleep:

- Read your goal out loud;

- Look at the picture that you have drawn;

- Read the description of your dream out loud;

- Close your eyes and imagine yourself living out your dream.

"Is that clear, young one?"

"Yes Sir," said Taran. He took the parchment, thanked the Oracle again and emerged from the cave into the spring sunshine.

As he made his way home, Taran clasped the parchment in his hand with a strange new sensation of excitement and happiness.

For as long as he could remember, he had dreamed about owning a stallion from the Alder Stables. Now, for the first time in his life, he felt as though his dream could actually become a reality because finally, he had a specific goal and a plan.

Taking Action

The next morning, Taran's alarm bell woke him from a deep sleep.

His alarm clock consisted of two chambers of water. Taran filled the first chamber when he went to sleep, and slowly the water trickled into the second chamber making it progressively heavier.

When the second chamber became heavy enough, it released a coiled spring that caused a hammer to strike a brass bell.

It was this bell that stirred him from his slumber.

Taran was still tired and felt like turning off his alarm and going back to sleep, but he knew that in order to make his dreams come true he had to put his plan into action.

He climbed out of bed and splashed some cold water onto his face. Then, sitting on the edge of his bed cover, he gave thanks for all the good things in his life:

- Thank you for my health and my body
- Thank you for my mother and Uncle Seth, and for the love and support they give me
- Thank you for my friends Olek and Tegan
- Thank you for our wonderful village
- Thank you for all the opportunities I have
- Thank you for the day ahead

As always, this helped him to wake up properly and made him look at the day in a positive light.

Taran then unrolled his goal parchment and in a loud, strong voice he read:

"I own a pure white stallion from the Alder Stables"

He looked at the picture of the stallion he had drawn, and then read the description of his dream out loud:

"I am enjoying the thrill of riding my pure white stallion through the hills of Etania. I can feel the cool breeze on my face and hear the wind roaring in my ears. I feel happy and proud as people from the village wave at us as we gallop by at full speed!"

After reading his description, Taran closed his eyes and imagined himself living out his dream.

In his mind's eye he saw himself riding his beautiful horse. He felt the cool wind against his face and felt the animal's powerful muscles coil and release beneath his legs. He imagined the sound of the stallion's mighty hooves thundering against the ground, and he saw the people of the village smiling and waving as he and his horse flashed by.

When Taran opened his eyes, he was filled with an incredible sense of drive and determination. All traces of sleep had vanished and he couldn't wait to get started on making his dream a reality.

He reviewed his plan which was:

1. Wake up early

2. Practice running up Falcon Ridge each morning before school

3. Gradually improve my running skills

4. Win the race

5. Collect my stallion from the Alder Stables

He had succeeded in waking up early thanks to his alarm bell, so now he knew it was time for his first practice session.

Taran quickly changed his clothes and moved quietly to the front door so he didn't wake his mother.

He emerged into the crisp morning air and was greeted by the sounds of birds calling in the distance. The wind rustled in the trees and his breath formed plumes of mist that rose high into the air as he set off at a brisk jog.

Before long he came to the base of Falcon Ridge where he found a wide-open clearing. Taran knew that the race would begin at this point.

Looking up at the imposing mountain in front of him, Taran felt a strange stirring in his stomach. He knew he had a lot of work to do and he was nervous about starting, but then he closed his eyes and once again imagined himself riding his pure white stallion.

With a surge of purpose, Taran began to run.

The slope was deceptively steep, and it wasn't long before Taran was breathing heavily. The perspiration began to bead on his brow as he continued to climb.

By the time Taran had reached the halfway point, he had slowed to a jog. His lungs were aching and his legs were burning. The perspiration ran down the side of his face, and he had to focus on just keeping his legs moving.

One step at a time…

Left foot…

Right foot…

Left foot…

Part of him wanted to stop. To just sit down and rest, but another part of him knew he had to continue.

As he jogged, he repeated to himself;

"Just one more step… Just one more step… Just one more step," and he continued to move slowly up the mountainside.

Eventually, Taran slowed to a walk but he refused to stop and rest. He focused on putting one foot in front of the other and then, as he rounded a bend in the path, he saw to his relief the large tilted boulder that marked the end of the race.

Taran took his last few steps and touched the boulder to confirm he had reached his objective. He paused for a moment with his hands on his knees, and then, taking a deep breath, he stood up and gave a mighty yell.

"WoooHoooo!!!" His cry echoed out across the valley.

Taran could feel his heart pounding against his chest and, although he was tired, he felt more alive than he had felt for a very long time.

Satisfied with his morning's work, Taran headed for home feeling great about himself, and the fact that he had followed his plan to the letter.

Later that night after a long day at school, Taran was tired and his muscles ached, but deep down he knew that this was all part of making his dream a reality.

Following the Oracle's instructions, Taran ended his day by reading his goal out loud:

"I own a pure white stallion from the Alder Stables"

Next, he looked at the picture of the stallion he had drawn. He then read out the description of his dream:

"I am enjoying the thrill of riding my pure white stallion through the hills of Etania. I can feel the cool breeze on my face and hear the wind roaring in my ears. I feel happy and proud as people from the village wave at us as we gallop by at full speed!"

And finally, he closed his eyes and imagined he was living out his dream. This was Taran's favorite part of the process. Each time he visualized his dream it seemed a little clearer and a little more real.

He also discovered that by visualizing his goal just before going to sleep, he often dreamed about his stallion and woke up feeling refreshed and alive.

In the weeks that followed, Taran acted on the Oracle's advice without faltering. Some mornings he found it very difficult to get out of bed, especially when it was cold. Part of him just wanted to stay snuggled up where it was warm, but he realized that to make his dream come true he sometimes had to do things that were difficult.

Each morning he made his way to Falcon Ridge and practiced running up the mountain to the tilted boulder.

Gradually, he found that his stamina improved and by the end of the second week he was able to jog all the way. By the end of the fourth week he could run the full length of the course.

Taran also found that each time he ran up the mountain, he noticed new things about the trail. For example, at one point, the course forked around a collection of boulders. By trying out both paths, Taran discovered that it was much quicker to take the right path than the left.

He also continued with his visualization exercises and came to love the feeling of closing his eyes and imagining his goal. Each time he visualized his future, it was as though he took another step towards making it a reality.

The Power of Focus

After eight weeks of dedicated training, Taran was feeling fit and confident. When he looked in the mirror he could see he was steadily growing healthier and stronger as the race day approached.

On a chilly morning, six weeks before the big day, Taran once again woke early and went through his morning routine. This was now so ingrained into his day that he did it almost without thinking.

He gave thanks for the good things in his life, he reviewed his goal, and he closed his eyes and visualized his dream as a reality. Then he changed his clothes and before he knew it, he was once again at the base of Falcon Ridge.

The day was cold and grey. A thin mist clung to the side of the mountain and rain-laden clouds gathered ominously overhead. Taran shook his head to clear away the last remnants of sleep and began his training.

Once again he fell into a familiar rhythm as he ran. With each step he recited a phrase that made him feel strong and powerful:

"I am fit, I am strong, I am healthy"

"I am fit, I am strong, I am healthy"

"I am fit, I am strong, I am healthy"

As he climbed the mountain, the mist seemed to get thicker and Taran found it difficult to see the trail ahead. He pressed on, but as he rounded the last bend, his foot slipped on a dew-covered rock and twisted painfully beneath him.

Taran staggered to regain his balance and collapsed by the side of the trail with a thud. He grabbed his throbbing ankle with both hands and cursed under his breath.

After the initial pain had subsided, Taran tentatively tried to stand up, only to find that when he put weight on his left foot, a sharp pain shot up his leg and sent stars spinning around in front of his eyes.

Sitting down again quickly, Taran grimaced and tried to rub his ankle, only to find that it had swollen to the size of a small melon.

"Not now! Why do I have to get injured now?" he said desperately. Although he was worried about the race, he also had to face the much more immediate problem of getting back home.

Taran searched the area nearby and found a strong tree branch that had fallen to the ground. He dragged himself to the branch and stripped off the twigs to make a rudimentary crutch.

Pulling himself upright, Taran leaned heavily on his makeshift crutch and then, half hopping, half limping, he made his way down the side of the mountain.

~

Later that day, Taran lay in bed feeling miserable. He knew his chances of winning the race were over. The village healer had come to see Taran and had told him he would need to rest his leg for eight weeks.

"It's not fair!" thought Taran forlornly as he stared up at his bedroom ceiling. His ankle was still throbbing, and more than anything he was angry at himself for being so careless.

While he analyzed what had gone wrong, he noticed that the Oracle's calling stone was once again glowing red. The Oracle wanted to see Taran, but there was no way he would be able to climb Ridley Peak with his injured ankle.

How was he going to tell the Oracle what had happened? They had forged a Pact! What would the Oracle think of Taran when he didn't turn up? What if the villagers found out that Taran had dishonored a Pact? Would his reputation in the village be ruined forever?

These questions filled Taran's mind as he heard the muffled sound of voices coming from the kitchen. After a brief pause, Taran's bedroom door opened and Uncle Seth entered the room.

"What've ye done to yourself boyo?" said Uncle Seth.

He came to Taran's bedside and looked down at his raised foot, which was still swollen and now a dark shade of purple.

"I twisted my ankle this morning."

"That's a nasty sprain by the look of it lad. You'd better stay off it for a while."

Taran nodded in reply and then said, "Uncle Seth, can I ask you something?"

"Of course ye can lad; what is it?"

Taran quickly told his uncle about the calling stone and that the Oracle had summoned him to his cave. Uncle Seth listened carefully, then reached down and ruffled Taran's hair.

"Don't ye worry lad. I'll go up and see the Oracle tomorrow and let him know what's happened."

"Thanks Uncle Seth." Taran sighed with relief and lay back on his pillow. His uncle returned to the kitchen and Taran heard him talking to his mother.

Now that the problem of contacting the Oracle was under control, Taran's thoughts drifted back to the race and to the unavoidable fact that his chance of owning a pure white stallion was gone forever.

He closed his eyes and drifted off into a troubled sleep. In his mind's eye he saw Lomak winning the race while he stood on the sidelines supporting his weight on crutches.

The following day, Taran's depression deepened. He was still stuck in bed and all he could do was sit and watch as the rain fell in discouraging sheets against his window.

"It just isn't fair," Taran thought to himself for the hundredth time. He had worked so hard, and everything had been going along so well. Why did he have to have an accident and ruin everything?

After brooding with his negative thoughts for the entire day, it came as a relief when Uncle Seth returned in the evening.

"Did you see the Oracle?" asked Taran, sitting up in bed and feeling his ankle jar painfully with the sudden movement.

"Aye lad. I saw the Oracle and told him what happened."

"What did he say?"

"He didn't say a lot to tell ye the truth. He said ye should look after yourself and he asked me to give ye this." Uncle Seth reached inside his heavy coat and pulled out a scroll of parchment.

"Thanks Uncle Seth," said Taran taking the scroll and placing it by the side of his bed, "I'll read it later."

"Make sure you do lad," said Uncle Seth with a nod.

"And thanks for going to see the Oracle for me Uncle Seth, I don't know what I would have done without you."

"Well, that's what families are for lad. Now I'd best be off. I've got to fire up the bellows for a big job tomorrow."

"Bye Uncle Seth, and thanks again."

"Bye boyo," and with that Uncle Seth left Taran alone with the Oracle's scroll.

The next morning, Taran looked down at the scroll that lay next to his bed. He wasn't sure whether he really wanted to read another 'lesson of wisdom' now that his chances of winning the race were over, but eventually boredom and curiosity got the better of him and he opened the scroll.

Focus not on the problem at hand, but rather on the solution

On the back of the parchment, the Oracle had written a note to Taran which read:

Young one,

When problems arise as they surely will, do not fall into the trap of focusing on your misfortune. Instead, focus on finding a solution, modify your plan and continue your journey.

The Oracle

Taran rolled up the scroll and placed it on his bedside table. He adjusted his pillow and lay back to look up at his favorite part of the ceiling.

As the day dragged slowly by, Taran reflected on the Oracle's lesson and realized he had indeed been focusing on his problem, rather than looking for a solution. He started to wonder if there was something he could do to make his injury heal more quickly.

When the village healer visited that afternoon, Taran asked him for advice. The healer stroked his beard thoughtfully, and then informed Taran that his ankle might improve more rapidly if he stretched it gently and applied a cold compress.

This was all Taran needed to hear.

With the Oracle's message still fresh in his mind, he took out a blank piece of parchment and rewrote his goal with a modified plan. His new plan was:

1. Do my stretches every morning

2. Apply a cold compress every day

3. Get strong again

4. Wake up early

5. Practice running up Falcon Ridge each morning before school

6. Gradually improve my running skills

7. Win the race

8. Collect my stallion from the Alder Stables

The very act of creating this new plan gave Taran a boost of self-confidence and a fresh sense of purpose. He was no longer just sitting around passively waiting for his ankle to heal.

He was now taking charge of the situation and doing everything he could to improve his chances of recovering in time for the race.

That night Taran asked his mother to soak an old rag in water and to leave it out on the porch.

By morning the frigid mountain air had transformed the rag into a perfect cold compress for Taran's ankle.

This compress, combined with his stretches, had an incredible impact on the rate of Taran's recovery. Within three days the swelling had subsided, and by the end of the week he was back on his feet.

With his new plan also came a new attitude. Taran realized he had been wasting his time feeling sorry for himself, instead of focusing on what he could do to improve his situation.

He also discovered that the moment he adopted a new, positive outlook, the attitude of the people around him changed as well.

After the accident, Taran's mother had sat with him and listened to him complain, but now she encouraged him to get up and get going.

The first time the village healer visited he seemed aloof and uninterested, but when Taran told him about the race, the healer's attitude changed. It turned out he had been a runner when he was younger and was keen to help Taran in any way he could. He began to drop in to see how Taran was doing, and even gave him some special herbal ointment to try.

A week later, Taran was walking without a limp and was ready to resume his morning training sessions.

His first sessions were very tentative. He started out by just walking to the base of Falcon Ridge and back again. Then, each morning, he extended his walk a little further up the mountain.

Before long, Taran was able to walk all the way to the tilted boulder at the top of Falcon Ridge. After a week of slow walking, he increased his pace to a gentle jog. Gradually, with each training session, his strength and self-confidence returned.

Occasionally he got frustrated by the rate of his progress and tried to start running again. When this happened he ended up stiff and sore, and realized he couldn't force his body to recover more quickly than it was able to. Taran came to understand that the key to his recovery was consistent application and patience.

His goal parchment and visualization exercises helped a great deal as well. Each day he visualized himself as being fit, strong and healthy. In his mind's eye he saw himself running up the mountain and claiming his white stallion from the Alder Stables.

As the weeks passed, Taran steadily increased his speed until he was once again running all the way to the top of Falcon Ridge. He was now confident of making a full recovery before the big race.

Taran hated to think what would have happened if he had not made the decision to focus on finding a solution, instead of dwelling on his problem.

He knew he would most probably have still been lying in bed, staring up at the ceiling and complaining about how unfair life was.

By adopting a positive mind-set and by modifying his plan to cater for his new situation, Taran had more than halved his recovery time.

Summer Solstice Eve

The day before the Summer Solstice, Taran's calling stone again turned red and he made his way back to the Oracle's cave.

He was amazed at how easy the journey was after all the training he had been doing.

When he entered the cave, the Oracle beamed at him and said, "You are looking well young one."

"Thank you Sir," replied Taran, feeling a small glow of satisfaction and pride. His mother and Uncle Seth had also commented on how much extra muscle he had put on through his regular training, and Taran felt great about himself and his newfound fitness.

"I can see you have been following your plan diligently young one."

"Yes Sir, I have. I have not missed a single day of training since recovering from my accident, and I have done my visualization exercises every morning and evening."

"Excellent. And so the race takes place tomorrow?"

"Yes, it starts at dusk in the clearing at the base of Falcon Ridge."

"And how do you feel about the race young one?"

"I feel as though I have done everything I can possibly do to prepare for it," said Taran, "I thought I would be nervous, but I'm not."

"Preparation is the antidote for nervousness young one. If you are prepared and have done the hard work, you do not need to be nervous."

"To tell you the truth, after visualizing my dream so often, I can't wait for tomorrow!" said Taran smiling broadly. He was confident, he was fit, and he knew that he was ready.

"You have learnt your lessons well, Taran Eldridge. Remember all you have learnt, and may the Gods be with you."

The Race

Taran was again standing in the clearing at the base of Falcon Ridge. He had stood in the very same spot nearly every morning for the past fourteen weeks, but this time he was not alone.

It was the eve of the Summer Solstice and the clearing was filled with the sights and sounds of the village celebrations.

A group of minstrels filled the air with lively music, while stilt-walkers and acrobats entertained the crowds. The entire village had turned out for the occasion, and little children chased each other in circles screeching with delight.

Around the perimeter of the clearing, oil lamps cast flickering shadows across the ground as dusk approached.

Taran looked up at the mountain that had once seemed so foreboding, and felt like he was visiting an old friend.

Around him many of the village children were looking at Falcon Ridge for the first time, and Taran could sense the apprehension in their eyes.

The only person who did not seem perturbed was Lomak, who stood away from the main group staring into the distance. He had grown since Taran had seen him last.

Lomak caught Taran's eye and walked straight towards him.

"I heard you been practicing kid," said Lomak in a rough voice.

"I've been doing a bit," replied Taran, meeting Lomak's stare evenly.

"Well, it ain't gonna do you any good, 'cause I'm going to whip you!" With that, Lomak turned and walked away.

Taran's insides churned and his blood boiled. If Lomak's words had been meant to unnerve him, they did exactly the opposite – now Taran was determined to beat him.

A stage had been erected in the centre of the clearing, and as the village Elders made their way onto the platform, a hush fell across the crowd.

"Welcome people of Etania!" called out the chief Elder. "Welcome to the eve of the Summer Solstice and to the greatest race ever!" The crowd clapped and cheered their approval.

"As you all know, this year's event is being supported by the Alder Stables, and as an incentive to our young contestants, here is what they will be competing for!"

There was a loud fanfare of trumpets and a stirring in the crowd as the most beautiful stallion Taran had ever seen was led into the clearing.

The horse was pure white, and every muscle in his powerful body seemed to glisten with grace and strength. The stallion flicked his noble head and pawed at the ground nervously.

It was the horse Taran had seen in his mind's eye every day since he had first met the Oracle. It was the horse of his dreams.

"And so..." said the chief Elder, "whoever reaches the summit of Falcon Ridge first will become the proud owner of this beautiful animal!" The crowd clapped excitedly.

"Ladies and gentlemen, are you ready for the race to begin?" called out the chief Elder.

"YES!" shouted the crowd in unison.

The runners took up their positions behind a line that had been drawn on the ground beneath a colorful banner. Taran was aware of Lomak away to his right.

"Are the runners ready?"

"YES!" replied the group of twenty-three children assembled behind the line.

The crowd was silent and the tension mounted...

"Go!" yelled the chief Elder.

Taran shot away to a flying start, his mind a flurry with ideas. But as soon as he took his first step up the incline, his thoughts cleared and he felt a sense of calm and purpose.

He knew this mountain. He knew every pothole and every bump. He knew how hard he should run at the beginning of the race and how much energy to keep in reserve.

The other children were running the race for the very first time, but Taran was on familiar ground. This was his mountain.

The incline became steeper and Taran noticed most of the children drop quickly behind. Soon there were only two runners left in contention, Taran and Lomak.

Up and up they climbed. Taran felt the familiar burning in his legs and his heart hammered against his rib cage.

From the corner of his eye, Taran could see Lomak as a shadowy figure just a few paces behind. He was fast, but Taran was confident.

At various vantage points along the trail, villagers had taken up positions to cheer and encourage the runners. Taran was vaguely aware of his friends Olek and Tegan calling out his name and urging him forward.

Higher and higher they climbed. Taran soon lost all track of time and turned his entire focus towards just making it to the next oil lamp as quickly as possible.

Ahead, the path reached a fork that separated around a familiar collection of boulders. Taran could sense Lomak just a few steps away.

Drawing on his experience, Taran took the path to the right. As he did so, he heard the sound of Lomak's footsteps diminish. He could tell without looking that Lomak had taken the left path!

Taran knew that this was his chance. He gritted his teeth and pumped his arms and legs as hard and as fast as he could.

When the two paths eventually converged, Taran risked glancing over his shoulder and saw that his plan had worked. He was now a good ten yards in front of Lomak!

Taran pushed on towards the summit.

With his body crying out for respite, he rounded the final bend and saw the tilted boulder that marked the end of the race.

His goal was in sight.

Torches had been lit to mark the finish line and a crowd of people started cheering loudly when they saw Taran appear.

He put his head down and prepared for the final assault. Then suddenly, like an apparition from a nightmare, Lomak was beside him.

Desperately, Taran summoned up his last remaining ounce of strength and tried to accelerate but his legs didn't respond. Time seemed to move in slow motion, and Taran watched in despair as Lomak edged ahead.

As Taran stumbled across the finish line, a bottomless chasm seemed to open up deep within his chest. His vision was blurred and his breath came in uneven gasps.

He felt hollow and empty. The cheering crowd seemed to be a million miles away as he fought back the tears.

Lomak had won the race.

Taran's Choice

Taran sat in bed and leaned against the wall. His head was downcast and it felt as though a heavy weight had settled in the centre of his chest. Several hours had passed since the end of the race and his eyes were swollen and red from crying.

Looking back on the day was difficult and painful. Everything seemed like a bad dream. He dimly remembered the faces of people coming in and out of focus saying, "Oh bad luck," and strangers patting him on the back.

Then he recalled the strong arms of Uncle Seth settling around his shoulders and guiding him out of the crowd to his mother, who held him tight and didn't say a word.

He had lost the race, and with it his chance to own the stallion of his dreams.

He had never felt so disappointed or let down before. He closed his eyes and thought, "It's not fair! I did so much work, I trained every morning, I read out my goals, I overcame my injury. I worked ten times harder than Lomak. I deserved to win. It's just not fair!" These thoughts played round and round Taran's mind as he drifted off into a restless sleep.

The next morning when Taran awoke, he saw that the calling stone was once again glowing red. The Oracle wanted to see him.

Taran felt his anger stir. The Oracle had lied to him. Everything he had taught Taran was a sham. It didn't work. He was just a foolish old man who lived in a cave and pretended to be wise.

As Taran dressed for the day, his anger grew. He would go and see the Oracle, and he would tell him exactly what he thought about his scrolls of wisdom and his advice.

On his way to the Oracle's cave, Taran clenched his goal parchment in his hand and repeatedly went over the events of the previous day in his mind. Each time he did so, he reinforced his view that the Oracle was to blame for everything that had happened. By the time he reached the Oracle's abode, Taran was furious.

He entered the cave without being asked and in a loud angry voice he said, "Everything you told me was a lie! It didn't work! I did everything you said and I lost the race."

To emphasize his point, Taran threw his goal parchment onto the table before continuing, "Lomak won just like he always does. I trained, I read out my goal every morning and every night and I still lost!" His words came out in a torrent of pain and resentment as the tears welled up in his eyes once more.

The Oracle looked at Taran and smiled a sad smile.

"And so, young one, we come to the most important lesson of all."

"No! No more lessons, no more scrolls. I don't want to do this anymore."

"Remember young one, you are bound by a Pact."

Taran started to complain but he knew the Oracle was right. He sat down at the table while the old man brought forward another ancient scroll.

"The Fourth Lesson of Wisdom," said the Oracle. Taran reluctantly opened the scroll to read:

The most important
secret of success is
learning how
to fail

"What is that supposed to mean?" asked Taran in an exasperated tone.

"Let me explain young one… Throughout your life, events will occur that are beyond your control. While you cannot control the events of your life, you can *always* control your responses to these events.

"For example, imagine the mill was closed for a day and the two men who worked there were sent home. The closing of the mill was an event that neither of the men could control. But what they did have control over was their response to this event.

"The first man's response was to get angry and annoyed. He went home and yelled at his children and spent the entire day complaining about the situation. The outcome he created through his response was that he and his family were miserable.

"The second man's response was to see the event as a chance to spend some time with his family. He went home and organized to go out with his children. They went down to the river Minrod and spent the whole day fishing, telling stories and laughing. The outcome the second man created through his response was that he and his family were happy, and also had a wonderful meal of fresh fish.

"The two men experienced the same event, but due to their different responses, they created completely different outcomes.

"Now, let's talk about a real event that has just happened to you. You set a goal, you worked very hard, but for some reason you did not win the race. This was an event that was beyond your control.

"What is your response to this event going to be young one?"

Taran said nothing.

"Everyone at some stage of their life goes through a similar experience to the one you have just been through. They set themselves a goal, they work very hard to achieve it, and for some reason, things don't work out the way they had hoped.

"Most people are so disappointed and disillusioned by this experience that they give up on their dream. They become so afraid of failing that they decide it is safer and easier never to set goals again.

"Successful people are different. They too are faced with the event many people call 'failure' but if things don't work out, they do not take it personally. They understand it is just their plan that failed, not *them*. Instead of giving up on their dream, they simply create a new plan and try again."

"But how can I create a new plan to win a race that has already been run?" asked Taran doubtfully.

"Your goal was not to win the race young one. Your goal was to own a stallion from the Alder Stables."

"Yes, but how can I do that without winning the race?"

"You need a new plan."

"How do I get a new plan?"

"The same way you got your first one – by asking the Question of Power."

Taran hesitated. He knew deep down that what the Oracle was saying made sense, but after the pain of losing the race, he wasn't entirely sure he was ready to try again. The Oracle observed Taran's hesitation and asked,

"What is it young one?"

"I'm afraid," admitted Taran. He knew it was the truth. He had been badly hurt by the experience of losing the race and he was afraid to try again.

"It is natural to be afraid, and this is your biggest test. Are you willing to go after what you are afraid of? Are you willing to risk failing again in order to succeed? Or will you choose to give up on your dream so you never have to risk failing again?"

Taran closed his eyes. The pain of losing the race was still there and so too was the fear of trying again, but he realized he really did have a choice.

He could give up on his dream of owning a stallion, and spend his life reliving his race failure. Or, he could decide he still wanted to make his dream a reality. He could decide to create a new plan and try again.

Taran's emotions churned and thoughts raced through his mind at a million miles an hour.

For the first time since the race he once again saw a vision of his horse, and with this vision came a sense of clarity and calm. In his heart he knew he still desperately wanted to own a pure white stallion from the Alder Stables.

He opened his eyes, took a deep breath and said, "I will create a new plan and try again."

"Excellent, young one," replied the Oracle, and he smiled at Taran warmly. "But before we proceed, you must first complete your original goal parchment."

Taran unrolled his parchment and smoothed out the creases he had created by gripping it so tightly on his way to the Oracle's cave.

"Now, draw another line across the bottom of your parchment, and write the words, 'Lessons Learnt' and 'Result'. After doing as the Oracle asked, Taran's parchment looked like this:

My Goal	My Plan
I own a pure white stallion from the Alder Stables	To achieve my goal I will:
	1. Wake up early
	2. Practice running up Falcon Ridge each morning before school
	3. Gradually improve my running skills
"I am enjoying the thrill of riding my pure white stallion through the hills of Etania. I can feel the cool breeze on my face and hear the wind roaring in my ears. I feel happy and proud as people from the village wave at us as we gallop by at full speed!"	4. Win the race
	5. Collect my stallion from the Alder Stables
	Target Date
	22/06/18
Lessons Learnt	**Result**

"Now young one, under the heading 'Result' I want you to write;

'This plan didn't work. I need a new plan.'

Taran followed the Oracle's instructions.

"Now, take a moment, and think about what you have learnt from the experience you have just been through." Taran thought about everything the Oracle had said, then under the 'Lessons Learnt' heading he wrote:

If my plan doesn't work, it doesn't mean that I have to give up my dream. It just means that I need a new plan.

Taran's completed parchment looked like this:

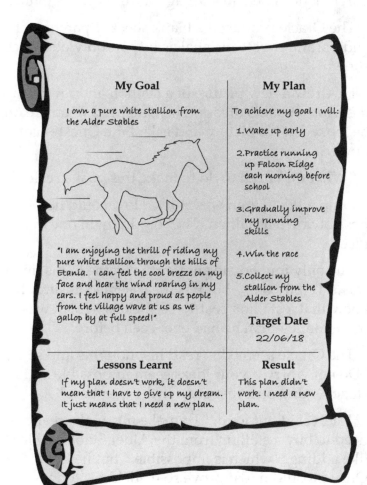

My Goal

I own a pure white stallion from the Alder Stables

"I am enjoying the thrill of riding my pure white stallion through the hills of Etania. I can feel the cool breeze on my face and hear the wind roaring in my ears. I feel happy and proud as people from the village wave at us as we gallop by at full speed!"

My Plan

To achieve my goal I will:

1. Wake up early

2. Practice running up Falcon Ridge each morning before school

3. Gradually improve my running skills

4. Win the race

5. Collect my stallion from the Alder Stables

Target Date

22/06/18

Lessons Learnt

If my plan doesn't work, it doesn't mean that I have to give up my dream. It just means that I need a new plan.

Result

This plan didn't work. I need a new plan.

"Very good young one. Now it is time to put this parchment aside and start again from the beginning."

The Oracle produced a blank sheet of parchment and Taran rewrote his goal as he had previously been shown.

He drew a new picture of a stallion and rewrote the description of his dream. Then, taking a deep breath, he looked at his picture and asked the Question of Power.

"What do I need to do to make this goal a reality?"

For a while, Taran was stuck. How could he possibly own a stallion if he couldn't win one in a race?

The only immediate answer that came to his mind was, "To buy one," but this idea seemed absurd. He knew that a stallion cost 1,000 shekels, which was more money than he had ever seen before.

The Oracle seemed to read his thoughts and said, "Do not worry if your ideas seem impossible at this stage, young one. Just answer the question."

Taran said out loud, "To make my goal a reality I need to buy a stallion from the Alder Stables." He felt like adding, "which is impossible," but he knew the Oracle would not approve so he held his tongue.

"Good, now ask the Question of Power again."

Taran said, "What do I need to do to buy a stallion from the Alder Stables?"

As the question hung in the air, the obvious answer popped into Taran's mind. Looking directly into the Oracle's sparkling eyes he said.

"To buy a stallion from the Alder Stables I need to earn 1,000 shekels."

The Oracle said nothing but his smile broadened. Taran continued.

"What do I need to do to earn 1,000 shekels?" He paused for a moment and again answered his own question.

"To earn 1,000 shekels I need to get a job and save every shekel I make."

Taran asked the Question of Power again:

"What do I need to do to get a job?" Taran wasn't sure what was involved with getting a job but he did know where he could start.

"To get a job I need to ask the store owners in the village if they are looking to hire someone."

"Excellent, young one. It sounds like you have the makings of a new plan," said the Oracle.

Taran thought about what the Question of Power had revealed and wrote down the following plan on his parchment:

1. Ask all the store owners in the village if they need someone to help out in the mornings or after school

2. Get a job

3. Save every shekel I make

4. Buy my stallion from the Alder Stables

Taran sat back when he was done and said, "There is only one problem with this plan."

"And what is that, young one?"

"If I make one shekel a day, I will make five shekels a week. That means I will make 250 shekels a year which means it will take me four years to make enough money to buy my stallion!"

"You are right, young one. It is a big commitment and not one to be taken lightly. You may have to work long and hard to achieve your dream."

Taran sat back and rested his chin in his hands. Four years was a long time, and it would probably mean he would not be able to play with his friends after school or enjoy his favorite sport of Trelak.

"It would have been a lot easier if I had just won the race," said Taran remorsefully.

"Looking back will never help you achieve the goals that lie in your future, young one," said the Oracle.

Taran nodded his head, and turning back to his parchment, he wrote down a target date four years in the future. His completed manuscript looked like this:

My Goal

I own a pure white stallion from the Alder Stables

"I am enjoying the thrill of riding my pure white stallion through the hills of Etania. I can feel the cool breeze on my face and hear the wind roaring in my ears. I feel happy and proud as people from the village wave at us as we gallop by at full speed!"

My Plan

To achieve my goal I will:

1. Ask all the store owners in the village if they need someone to help out in the mornings or after school.

2. Get a job

3. Save every shekel I make

4. Buy my stallion from the Alder Stables

Target Date
22/06/22

Taran left the Oracle's cave feeling better than he had felt since losing the race. The heavy weight in his chest had lightened and he grasped his new parchment firmly in his hand.

It wasn't going to be easy, but he was once again determined to do whatever it took to make his dream a reality.

The Alder Stables

On his way home from the Oracle's cave, Taran decided to stop by the Alder Stables.

As he approached the long, wooden fence and looked out across the beautiful green lawns, Taran felt a familiar yearning in his heart.

In the confines of the stable grounds he could see two apprentices riding a pair of magnificent black horses. Taran held his breath as the powerful animals thundered past him, kicking up clods of dirt high into the air. From his vantage point he felt like he was looking into a magical world.

Over by the gate, Taran caught sight of one of the older trainers. He was lifting sacks of what looked like horse feed onto a wagon. From the bright red color of his face it was clear he was struggling.

Taran approached the gate and asked, "Excuse me Sir, would you like a hand with that?"

The old man stopped and looked up, "I'd be much obliged lad," he replied with a sigh. He took out a handkerchief and mopped the perspiration from his brow.

Taran passed though the gates of the Alder Stables and approached the wagon. He picked up the first sack and immediately understood why the old man was having problems. They were heavy! Taran was amazed that the old man had managed to lift them at all. There were five bags left to load onto the wagon and he quickly had them safely secured.

"Thank you lad, I think you saved my back," said the old man with a wink.

"You're welcome Sir," replied Taran.

"Ain't you the lad from the Summer Solstice Race?" asked the old trainer with a sideways glance.

"I did enter the race Sir, but I came second," replied Taran sadly.

"Aye, well you put up a grand fight lad, you should be proud of yourself."

"Thank you," said Taran with half a smile.

"What's your name lad?" asked the old man.

"Taran Eldridge, Sir," replied Taran.

"Any relation to Seth Eldridge?"

"Yes Sir, he's my uncle," replied Taran.

"Your uncle does fine work lad. I'd say he's the best blacksmith in all of Etania."

Taran smiled proudly, "Yes Sir, he is."

"Well Taran Eldridge, we could use a strong lad like you around this place," said the trainer casually, while he folded his handkerchief and placed it in his pocket, "I don't suppose you'd be looking for a part-time job?"

Taran was stunned. He couldn't believe his ears. He had just written a new plan which involved getting a job, and now completely out of the blue the old trainer had offered him the job of his dreams.

For a moment Taran was lost for words before replying, "I would love to work here Sir."

"Excellent! Then you can start tomorrow. By the way, my name is Rohan Alder," said the old man shaking Taran's hand firmly.

Once again Taran's senses reeled. The old man smiling before him wasn't just a horse trainer. He was Rohan Alder, the owner of the Alder Stables and one of the richest men in all of Etania!

"It's nice to meet you Mr. Alder," stammered Taran nervously. Rohan Alder laughed a big booming laugh.

"Don't look so surprised lad! I still enjoy getting out here and doing my share of the work. It helps keep me sane."

"I can understand that – it's a beautiful place," said Taran looking out across the grounds. "What time would you like me to be here tomorrow?"

"Now what if I said at sun up?" asked Rohan Alder looking Taran straight in the eye.

Taran could tell the question was a test. Without hesitating he replied, "I'll be here at sun up."

"Excellent Taran, that's what I like to hear. I think you and I are going to get along just fine."

Taran shook Rohan Alder's hand again before racing home to share his incredible news with his mother and Uncle Seth. He was going to work at the Alder Stables!

A New Plan

In the days and weeks that followed, Taran worked at the Alder Stables each morning before school. His new job meant he had to wake up before sunrise, but he still made time to practice his morning success routine.

He began each day by giving thanks for all the good things in his life, which now included a job he loved. Then he took out his parchment and read his goal out loud.

I own a pure white stallion from the Alder Stables

Next, he looked longingly at the picture of the stallion he had drawn and read the description of his dream.

"I am enjoying the thrill of riding my pure white stallion through the hills of Etania. I can feel the cool breeze on my face and hear the wind roaring in my ears. I feel happy and proud as people from the village wave at us as we gallop by at full speed!"

After reading his goal description, Taran closed his eyes and visualized his dream in vivid detail.

The pain of losing the race did not disappear overnight, but gradually as Taran repeatedly read and visualized his goal, he stopped looking back at what had happened, and started looking forward to making his dream a reality.

Taran came to realize that the Oracle had been right. The reason he had felt so bad after losing the race was because he thought he had lost his only chance of ever owning a stallion.

He now understood that if a plan didn't work, it did not mean he had to give up on his dream.

Instead, he could create a new plan and try again. This gave him an immense feeling of confidence. Instead of just 'hoping' he would reach his goal, he now knew that as long as he held onto his dream and kept reviewing and improving his plan, he *would* eventually make his dream a reality.

Taran earned one shekel a day at the Alder Stables and each morning he would come home and place his shekel in a wooden box that Uncle Seth had given him for his birthday.

He worked hard at the stables and always did his very best. If there was something that needed to be done, Taran would always be the first to volunteer, and he never complained if he was asked to do additional tasks.

Rohan Alder and the other trainers took notice of the way Taran worked, and as the weeks turned into months, Taran moved from cleaning out the stables to helping the apprentices and trainers get the horses ready for their morning training sessions.

It was fun, although it was also a lot of hard work. As winter approached it was difficult to wake up before sunrise, and the training sessions were long and bitterly cold. Nevertheless, by reading his goal every morning, Taran stayed focused and his commitment never wavered.

Each week Taran reviewed his plan and checked on the money he was collecting.

By the end of three months he had 60 shekels.

By the end of six months he had 120 shekels.

He still had a long way to go before he got to his 1,000 shekel goal, but day by day, week by week, Taran knew he was moving steadily closer to making his dream come true.

One morning, while Taran was grooming and watering a large black stallion named Ember, he heard a terrible commotion coming from outside the stalls.

He tied the horse securely in its stable and went to see what was causing the ruckus.

As he emerged from the stables, Taran stopped dead in his tracks. At the entrance gate, Mr. Alder was shouting and gesturing angrily at a man who was holding the reins of a pure white stallion.

It was the stallion from the Summer Solstice Race.

Taran recognized the man holding the reins as Lomak's father. Even from a distance Taran could see there was something terribly wrong with the animal.

The once beautiful steed was emaciated, and his ribs showed through his coat. The proud animal tried to lift his noble head but was too weak. He hobbled forward on a damaged front leg to nibble at a tuft of nearby grass.

Rohan Alder and Lomak's father were hollering at each other at the top of their voices. Taran had never seen Mr. Alder look so furious. From the volume of their conversation it quickly became apparent what was going on.

Mr. Alder was outraged at the way Lomak's father had mistreated the stallion. It was clear from the horse's forlorn state that he had not been properly fed and had been terribly overworked and abused.

At the same time, Lomak's father was yelling at Mr. Alder, complaining that the horse was useless and demanding a new horse as a replacement.

At the sight of the poor broken animal, Taran got a lump in his throat and struggled to hold back the tears. It was so unfair that this beautiful horse had had to endure such cruel treatment. If Taran had won the race he would have loved the stallion with all his heart, but instead, Lomak's family had made the animal's life a living hell.

The argument at the gate raged on. Having realized he was not going to get a replacement horse, Lomak's father was now demanding Mr. Alder buy back the stallion, even though he had not paid a cent for the animal.

"You won't find a buyer for that horse in all of Etania after what you've done to him," roared Mr. Alder.

"Well, if that's the way you feel about it Alder, I'm taking the lazy beast straight to the knackery. So either you buy back your useless stallion or it dies," bellowed Lomak's father so vehemently that specks of saliva flew from his snarling mouth.

In the silent pause that followed this threat, Taran stepped forward and said in a loud voice,

"I'll give you 120 shekels for the horse."

Lomak's father turned his head and stared at Taran, his eyes narrowing menacingly.

"And where are you going to get 120 shekels boy?"

The blood pounded in Taran's ears but he fought to keep his emotions at bay.

"I have 120 shekels from working here for the past six months and I will give them to you today in exchange for the stallion."

Mr. Alder moved away from the gate and walked over to Taran. He put his hand on Taran's shoulder and lowered his voice to a whisper.

"Be careful lad, that horse is hurt bad. I don't know if that front leg will ever heal. He may have to be put down for his own good."

Taran looked up slowly and said, "I have to try and help him, Mr. Alder. I just have to."

Rohan Alder looked Taran in the eye and their shared love of horses communicated far more than mere words ever could.

"Alright lad, you do what you think is best and you can keep him here while he mends."

Mr. Alder turned back towards Lomak's father and shouted, "Well, you heard the boy's offer. One hundred-and-twenty shekels is more than you'll ever get from the knackery. You'd be a fool not to accept."

Lomak's father stared at Taran in angry silence before saying, "Alright boy. You can have the good-for-nothing beast for 120 shekels, as long as I get the money today."

Taran moved forward, took the horse's reins and led him into the stables. He found a fresh stall and filled a trough with feed for the starving animal.

As the stallion ate gratefully, Taran carefully combed out the sties and burrs from his mane and rubbed down his scarred white coat.

Somehow, the horse seemed to know that his days of torment were over, and Taran felt a warm glow inside as the animal whinnied softly and turned his head to gently nuzzle Taran's hand.

The Stallion

That night, before going to sleep, Taran took out his parchment as usual and looked down at the words he had written long ago.

I own a pure white stallion from the Alder Stables

He smiled to himself and enjoyed a wonderful feeling of satisfaction as he realized that the goal he had been focusing on for so long was now a reality. He really did own a pure white stallion from the Alder Stables!

He had thought it would take him four years to buy his own horse, but in the end he had achieved his goal in just six months. Taran could never have imagined things would turn out the way they had.

In the days that followed, Taran returned to the stables each evening after school to help his horse recover from the ordeal he had experienced at the hands of Lomak's family.

The head trainer set the animal's leg in a splint and slowly the stallion began to respond to the treatment and tender loving care of his new owner.

Taran named his horse Spirit, and as time passed, the stallion began to live up to his name.

Within two months, Taran was able to ride his horse gently around the grounds of the Alder Stables. With each ride, the stallion grew stronger and Taran felt the horse's powerful muscles begin to respond to the good food and regular exercise.

Gradually, Spirit began pulling at his reins, eager to feel the freedom and joy of galloping again, but Taran urged his horse to be patient and to progress one step at a time.

After four months of steady and methodical progress, Taran knew his horse was ready.

The following morning the trainers and apprentices assembled at the gates as Taran led Spirit from the stables. Mr. Alder stood at the head of the group and made a little speech as Taran mounted his steed.

"Today is a very auspicious day at the Alder Stables," began Mr. Alder, enjoying the occasion. "Ten months ago Taran started working here and I think you'll all agree he's done a fine job." There was a loud chorus of agreement from the trainers, and Taran felt his cheeks flush with embarrassment.

"Many of you will remember the Summer Solstice Race last year in which Taran just missed out on winning a stallion." There were many nods from the assembled group.

"Well, to his credit, Taran didn't give up on his dream. He worked hard and when the opportunity presented itself, he was able to buy his stallion and save the poor animal from a cruel fate."

Mr. Alder continued with gusto, "What's more, Taran has been diligent in coming in after school to take care of his horse and today he is going to take Spirit for his first ride in the valley." There was a round of clapping and cheering as one of the apprentices opened the main gate.

Mr. Alder finished his speech by saying, "Let's hear three cheers for Taran and Spirit!"

"Hip Hip, HOORAY"

"Hip Hip, HOORAY"

"Hip Hip, HOORAY!"

Taran swelled with pride and smiled at his friends before urging Spirit forward. The powerful stallion responded immediately and shot forward like a bolt of lightning.

In a flash they were past the gate and riding through the hills of the valley. Taran whooped with delight as he felt the wind in his hair and the freedom of riding his very own stallion.

Taran wasn't the only one having the time of his life. Spirit tossed his head and whinnied with joy at the turn of events that had led him to his new life and his new owner.

Together, Taran and Spirit galloped through the valley sharing the thrill of freedom and discovery.

As they neared the village, a small boy walking hand-in-hand with his mother looked up at the sound of thundering hooves and waved eagerly at Taran. Taran smiled and waved back, and in that instant he realized he was living his dream!

"I am enjoying the thrill of riding my pure white stallion through the hills of Etania. I can feel the cool breeze on my face and hear the wind roaring in my ears. I feel happy and proud as people from the village wave at us as we gallop by at full speed!"

Taran had achieved his goal and was living his dream exactly as he had envisaged it. He felt more alive and happy than he had ever felt before in his entire life.

A Fond Farewell

The following morning Taran awoke with a sense of happiness and fulfillment. He gave thanks for all the good things in his life which now included his beautiful horse Spirit.

After breakfast, Taran decided to go and visit the Oracle. If it hadn't been for his mentor none of this would have happened, and Taran wanted to share his success with the person who had made it all possible.

With a spring in his step and the sun climbing slowly over the hills surrounding the valley, Taran made his way to the Oracle's cave.

"Come in young one," said a familiar voice as Taran approached. The Oracle was sitting in a comfortable chair, reading a large book while sipping his herbal tea.

"I did it Sir, I did it!" said Taran smiling uncontrollably.

"Come, share your tale, young one," replied the Oracle laying aside his book and offering Taran a chair.

Taran sat down and described the events of the previous months. He told the Oracle how he had been offered a job only moments after creating his new plan. How he had worked hard at the Alder Stables, and most incredibly, how he had ended up buying Spirit.

"The Universe truly works in mysterious ways," said the Oracle with a broad smile. "I am not surprised by the tale you tell, but I am indeed very happy for you. Did you bring your goal parchment with you?"

"Yes Sir, I did." Taran reached into his coat and produced his parchment, which he opened out on the table.

"It is time to complete your plan, young one." As before, Taran ruled an extra line on his parchment and created the headings 'Lessons Learnt' and 'Result'.

"Now, take this quill and under the 'Result' heading write SUCCESS!" Taran wrote on his parchment with a sense of pride and satisfaction.

The Oracle smiled and said, "And finally, write down what you have learnt from pursuing this goal."

Taran paused for a moment and then wrote:

> I held on to my goal, created a new plan
> and made my dream come true!

His finished parchment looked like this:

My Goal

I own a pure white stallion from the Alder Stables

"I am enjoying the thrill of riding my pure white stallion through the hills of Etania. I can feel the cool breeze on my face and hear the wind roaring in my ears. I feel happy and proud as people from the village wave at us as we gallop by at full speed!"

My Plan

To achieve my goal I will:

1. Ask all the store owners in the village if they need someone to help out in the mornings or after school.

2. Get a job

3. Save every shekel I make

4. Buy my stallion from the Alder Stables

Target Date

22/06/22

Lessons Learnt

I held onto my goal, created a new plan and made my dream come true!

Result

SUCCESS!

"You have come a long way in the last year young one; tell me, what have you learnt from your experience?"

Taran thought about the Oracle's question carefully. So much had happened since the day they had first met.

"First of all I learnt that it feels great to start each day by giving thanks for the good things in my life." The Oracle nodded his agreement.

"Then I learnt how to identify my heart's desire and how to create a plan using the Question of Power."

"Next, I learnt to review my goal every morning and every evening. The part I enjoyed most was visualizing my dream as though it had already come true."

"Good," said the Oracle, "And what else?"

"Well, then I had my accident and I learnt that when problems come up, it's important to focus on finding a solution, rather than focusing on the problem itself.

"Is there anything else, young one?"

"Well, the most important lesson I learnt was when I lost the race. I thought that my dream was gone forever, but then you showed me that if my plan didn't work, it didn't mean I had to give up on my dream. It just meant I needed to create a new plan and try again."

"You have learnt your lessons well young one, and our Pact is now complete."

"Thank you for all your help and guidance Oracle," said Taran handing back the magical calling stone.

"You are very welcome, young one. Now go, and dream big dreams, and never let anyone tell you that you cannot make your dreams come true."

Taran grasped the Oracle's hand and shook it warmly before emerging from the cave.

The world was full of endless possibilities and as he made his way back home, Taran Eldridge was already planning his next goal.

The End

Dare To Dream!

I hope you enjoyed reading The Oracle's Secret as much as I enjoyed writing it. I'd like to take this opportunity to invite you to sign up for my free 'Dare To Dream' newsletter.

Each week you'll receive an email newsletter containing:

* FREE articles and special reports
* Strategies to help you achieve your dreams
* Interviews with successful individuals
* The latest tips and techniques for achieving success
* And Much More!

To subscribe, please visit:

www.AnthonyFernando.com

I look forward to helping you make *your* dreams a reality!

Anthony Fernando

About The Author

Dr. Anthony Fernando graduated from Monash University in Melbourne, Australia, where he was awarded the Dean's List Fellowship for Academic Excellence.

He went on to join Accenture, a global computer consulting firm, where he became a Senior Consultant specializing in enterprise application design and multimedia software development.

In 2002, Anthony started his own business developing educational computer software. His program 'Piano Is Fun' (www.PianoIsFun.com) is now used in 48 States of America and 34 countries around the world, including Aruba, Chile, Iceland, Mauritius, Trinidad & Tobago and Zimbabwe.

Most recently, Anthony has launched the website www.TheDontQuitPoem.com which is helping to spread hope and inspiration around the world.